This Book Belongs to

_____

_____

_____

BART SIMPSON 2012 ANNUAL

For information address
Bongo Comics Group
P.O. Box 1963, Santa Monica, CA 90406-1963

Published in the UK by Titan Books, a division of Titan Publishing Group,
144 Southwark St., London SE1 0UP, under licence from Bongo Entertainment, Inc.

FIRST EDITION: AUGUST 2011

ISBN: 9780857685285

1 3 5 7 9 10 8 6 4 2

Publisher: Matt Groening
Creative Director: Bill Morrison
Managing Editor: Terry Delegeane
Director of Operations: Robert Zaugh
Art Director: Nathan Kane
Art Director Special Projects: Serban Cristescu
Production Manager: Christopher Ungar
Assistant Art Director: Chia-Hsien Jason Ho
Production/Design: Karen Bates, Nathan Hamill, Art Villanueva
Staff Artist: Mike Rote
Administration: Ruth Waytz, Pete Benson
Legal Guardian: Susan A. Grode

PRINTED IN ITALY

BART SIMPSON™

ANNUAL 2012

Titan Books

YOUR LITTLE *STUNT* JUST RUINED $2,500.00 WORTH OF *LAWN*, AND YOU'RE GONNA *PAY BACK* EVERY *PENNY* STARTING WITH YOUR 'GATOR FARM'S *PROFITS!*

UH, GEE, HOMER, DID *YOU* EVER GET IN THIS MUCH *TROUBLE* WHEN *YOU* WERE A *KID?*

ATTABOY, BART, GET HOMER *DISTRACTED*, AND HE'LL *FORGET* ALL ABOUT HIS YARD!

WHAT DOES *THAT* HAVE TO DO WITH--

WELL, COME TO *THINK* OF IT, THERE *WAS* THAT TIME...

"IT HAPPENED BACK WHEN I WAS JUST A LITTLE OLDER THAN *YOU!* I WAS KNOWN AS A *SPUNKY* LI'L GUY..."

"*WOODSTOCK*"? WE ALREADY *WENT* TO WOODSTOCK! AND DON'T YOU *DARE* USE THAT "*SPUNKY*" ROUTINE ON ME!

YEAH, *REMEMBER*, POP?

"SIX DAYS OF PEACE, LOVE, UNDERSTANDING"...AND *MUD!* *ACRES* OF *MUD!*

YEAH, AND I'M STILL PLENTY *STEAMED* THAT SHA-NA-NA NEVER SHOWED UP! ANYWAY, I'LL GIVE *YOU* SOME "UNDER-STANDING," YOU HOPPED-UP HOOLIGAN!

"SO I WOUND UP DOING WHAT I USUALLY DID WHEN I WAS FEELING KINDA *LOW*..."

⋚SNIFF!⋚ ⋚SNIFF!⋚ MMM...*DONUTS*! I MAY BE *BROKE*, BUT THERE'S NOTHING BETTER THAN THE SMELL OF FRESH *LARD LAD DONUTS* IN THE MORNING!

MAKE LIKE A *DONUT* AND *ROLL* OUTTA HERE!

UH-OH! I WONDER WHAT'S *SHAKIN'* AT LARD LAD'S? UH, BESIDES THEIR WORLD-FAMOUS *LARD-SHAKES*, THAT IS!

WOW, CHECK OUT *THAT* GUY! I WONDER WHAT IT'D BE LIKE TO GET AS *FAT* AS THAT BIG *SLOB!?**

I HATE TO *DO* THIS, VERNON, BUT YOU GIVE ME NO *CHOICE*! YOU'VE BEEN EATING SO MANY *FREE* DONUTS, YOU'RE GONNA PUT ME *OUTTA BUSINESS*!

⋚SOB!⋚ *CHOMP!* ⋚SOB!⋚

*OH, YOU'LL *FIND OUT*, HOMEY-- WHEN YOU *GROW UP*--AND *OUT*!

HEY, WHY'D YOU *FIRE* THAT GUY, MR. LARD LAD MANAGER?

VERNON'S ALWAYS BEEN OUR OFFICIAL "LARD LAD" GUY! BUT HE'S GOTTEN SO *FAT*, HE'S TOO *BIG* TO FIT IN OUR *LARD LAD WALK-AROUND* SUIT ANYMORE!

VERNON WAS THE *FIRST* ONE WHO GOT CUT, BUT IT LOOKS LIKE I'VE GOTTA START TRIMMING MY ENTIRE *STAFF*!

"AND AN HOUR AFTER THAT..."

THIS HAS GOTTA BE THE *TOUGHEST* JOB IN THE WORLD! I'M PRACTICALLY *STEWING* IN MY OWN *JUICES!*

HEY, THAT PUTS ME IN THE MOOD FOR BEEF *STEW!*

"MEANWHILE, ACROSS THE STREET AT *KEEP ON DUNKIN'* DONUTS, UNFRIENDLY EYES STUDIED THE POOR LITTLE DONUT BOY..."

THAT *LARD LAD* KID'S STILL OUT THERE!

AW, DON'T PAY ANY ATTENTION TO HIM, BOSS! WITHIN A MONTH OR TWO, WE'LL PUT LARD LAD DONUTS COMPLETELY *OUT OF BUSINESS!*

WHY *WAIT?* WE'RE GONNA *SHUT DOWN* THOSE LAME LOSERS BEFORE OUR GRAND OPENING...OR MY NAME ISN'T *JIMMY MAPLELOG!*

AND WHAT BETTER PLACE TO *START* THAN WITH THEIR GREASY-HAIRED *MASCOT?!?*

"AT FIRST, I WAS *OBLIVIOUS* TO JIMMY MAPLELOG'S *TRICKS*..."

WHOAH! YOW! WOOP! YEEP!

PSST! I PUT SOME *FIRE ANTS* INTO THE KID'S *LARD LAD* SUIT! WATCH 'IM *DANCE!*

"THE KEEP ON DUNKIN' GANG STRUCK TIME AFTER TIME, BUT I THOUGHT I WAS JUST HAVING A STREAK OF BAD LUCK..."

OH BOY, IT'S TIME FOR *LUNCH!*

HEY, WHAT'S GOIN' ON HERE? I CAN'T REMOVE MY *HEADPIECE!*

WOW, THAT NEW *"NUTTY GLUE"* REALLY WORKS!

"...REALLY, *REALLY* BAD LUCK!"

NICE DOGGIES! ≶PUFF! PANT!≶ *GOOD* DOGGIES!

BOW-WOW! ARF! ARF! WOOF! WOOF!

≶CHUCKLE!≶ PUTTING A POUND OF *BACON* INSIDE THAT TWERP'S COSTUME WAS OUR BEST STUNT *YET!*

"AFTER A FEW HARROWING DAYS, I FINALLY *CAUGHT ON* TO THEIR *DIRTY TRICKS*..."

Y'KNOW, I'M STARTING TO THINK THESE "ACCIDENTS" ARE *NO ACCIDENT!*

THOSE GUYS FROM *KEEP ON DUNKIN' DONUTS* ARE TRYING TO PUT *LARD LAD DONUTS* OUT OF *BUSINESS!*

AND IF *LARD LAD* GOES OUT OF BUSINESS, THEN I'M OUT OF A *JOB!*

AND IF I'M OUT OF A *JOB*, THEN MY *DAD'S* GONNA *CLOBBER* ME! I'M *DOOMED!*

"*DESPERATE* FOR *ADVICE*, I TURNED TO MY BEST FRIEND, *BARNEY GUMBLE*..."

WHAT SHOULD I *DO*, BARNEY?

THE WAY I SEE THINGS, YOU'VE GOT *NO CHOICE* BUT TO *SHUT DOWN* THE *KEEP ON DUNKIN'* SHOP BEFORE THEY CAN DO THE SAME THING TO *LARD LAD!*

13

"SUDDENLY, I *NOTICED* SOMETHING..."

HEY, THE *SUN* IS COMING UP ALREADY! AND *LOOK* WHO'S *WAITING* OUTSIDE!

GRAND OPENI—

I'M SO *ANXIOUS* TO TASTE THESE NEW *DONUTS!*

ME TOO! THEY'RE 100% *ORGANIC!*

IF THEY'RE AS *YUMMY* AS THEY'RE *SUPPOSED* TO BE, I'LL GIVE THIS PLACE *FOUR STARS* IN MY *RESTAURANT REVIEW* FOR *THE SPRINGFIELD SHOPPER!*

LEAVE IT TO *ME,* SISTER. IF ANYONE KNOWS GOOD *DONUTS,* IT'S *COPS* LIKE ME!

OH, *MY!*

WHAT THE?!

YOU CAN SAY *THAT* AGAIN!

S'CUSE ME. PARDON ME. S'CUSE ME. PARDON ME...

COMIN' THROUGH!

COME *BACK* HERE, YOU BRATS! I'M GONNA *TWIST* YOUR *NECKS* INTO *ALL-MEAT CRULLERS,* THEN I'M--!

BZZZZT!

UH-OH.

"SOON, SPRINGFIELD'S *CHIEF HEALTH INSPECTOR* SHOWED UP TO *SHUT DOWN* THE STORE BEFORE IT EVER EVEN *OPENED!*"

LET'S TAKE A TRIP *DOWNTOWN,* BOYS. BUT *FIRST,* LET'S MAKE A STOP AT *LARD LAD DONUTS!*

MUST YOU ADD *INSULT* TO *INJURY?*

HA! HA! HA!

"LATER, THE FOLKS AT *LARD LAD DONUTS* EVEN THREW A *PARTY IN MY HONOR.*"

YOU *SAVED* LARD LAD, HOMEY! AND FOR *THAT,* I'M GIVING YOU A *GREAT BIG BONUS!*

WOO-HOO!

HEY, WHAT ABOUT *ME?*

"UNFORTUNATELY FOR *ME*, MY OWN FATHER WASN'T *NEARLY* AS PLEASED WITH ME."

WHAT DO YOU *MEAN*, YOUR *BONUS* WAS DOZENS OF FREE LARD LAD *DONUTS*?

YEAH, AND THEY WERE *DELICIOUS*!

BUT YOU STILL *OWE* ME A *SMALL FORTUNE*!

PROBLEM IS, AFTER *EATING* ALL THOSE DONUTS, I CAN'T *FIT* IN THAT LARD LAD SUIT ANYMORE, SO I GOT *FIRED*!

FIRED? WHY, I'LL ADD SOME "FIRE" TO YOUR *HEINIE*, YOU LARD-FILLED *LAYABOUT*!

UH, T-TAKE IT *EASY*, POP! ‡CHOKE!‡ REMEMBER YOUR *BLOOD PRESSURE*!

THROTTLE!

"WHICH *REMINDS* ME..."

WHY, I'LL ADD SOME "FIRE" TO YOUR *HEINIE*, YOU LARD-FILLED *LAYABOUT*!

GEE, THAT SOUNDS AWFULLY *FAMILIAR*!

I'VE GOT A *BETTER* IDEA, HOMER!

YOU GOTTA *ADMIT*...GRABBING A FEW DOZEN *DONUTS* IS *MUCH BETTER* THAN GRABBING MY *THROAT*!

MMM... DONUTS!

WELL, IF IT AIN'T HOMEY SIMPSON! HOWYA DOIN', KIDDO? STILL PACKIN' ON THE *POUNDS*, I SEE!

HEY, LOOK! THEY'RE BUILDING A NEW *KRUSTY KREME* DONUT SHOP RIGHT *ACROSS* THE *STREET*!

HMMM...I WONDER IF *THEY* NEED A MASCOT? HEH-HEH!

THE END!

LISA & BART SIMPSON in
THE PRINCESS PRINCIPLE

CAROL LAY
STORY & ART

ALAN HELLARD
COLORS

KAREN BATES
LETTERS

BILL MORRISON
EDITOR

18

I'VE GOT TO STUDY THIS PRINCESS PONY LINE, SO I CAN DESIGN THE BEST COSTUME!

GOOD...I'M THE FIRST ONE TO THINK OF THIS, SO THERE ARE PLENTY OF PRODUCTS TO LOOK AT!

ESS PALOOZA!

SHODDY CRAFTSMANSHIP... UTTERLY--

A PULL CORD...!

ZZZZZIP!

McBA IS BACK

★ Anything you desire is attainable if your heart is pure. ★

;GASP! IT'S A SIGN!

I WONDER WHAT ELSE SHE HAS TO TELL ME?!

AHEM!

HERE'S ANOTHER SIGN THAT MIGHT INTEREST YOU.

ONE PULL per PATRON This means YOU!

I'VE **GOT** TO KNOW WHAT **ELSE** SHE'LL SAY!

I HOPE I HAVE ENOUGH BABYSITTING MONEY...

-BUMP!

MALIBU STACY! I'M NOT BETRAYING YOU... **REALLY!**

WHATEVER YOU DREAM CAN BECOME REALITY IF YOU APPLY YOUR INTELLECT.

MAYBE THEY'RE **BOTH** RIGHT!

I'VE BEEN WAITING FOR YOU TO CROSS OVER TO THE PINK AND GIRLY SIDE, YOUNG LADY.

HAVE YOU SEEN THE LATEST PRINCESS PONY BOUDOIR BEAUTY SET? ONLY $37.99 PLUS TAX.

IT'S SO VAPIDLY POINTLESS!

BUT IT'S **PRETTY!** I WANT IT!

KA-CHING! THAT IS MUSIC TO MY POINTY VULCAN EARS.

Princess Pony

Boudoir Beauty

BUTT OUT! *THIS CONTEST* IS FOR *PRINCESSES* ONLY!

WHO-OA-A-A... CHILL, LIS.

I'LL KEEP CLEAR OF YOUR STUPID CONTEST.

NOT.

GOOD.

AND DON'T TELL MOM OR DAD, EITHER. THEY THINK WE HAVE ENOUGH PETS ALREADY.

MY LIPS ARE SEALED, YOUR HIGHNESS!

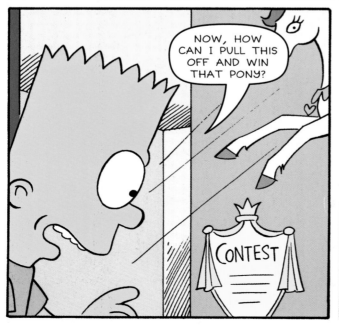

NOW, HOW CAN I PULL THIS OFF AND WIN THAT PONY?

ENTER, MY BOY, AND I WILL SCHOOL YOU IN ALL THINGS *PRINCESS PONY.*

SOUNDS STUPID, BUT *OKAY.*

AND DON'T FORGET YOUR WALLET.

IT'S TOO BAD I SPENT ALL OF MY ALLOWANCE ON *PRINCESS PONY* THINGS. THIS GOWN COULD REALLY USE A LOT MORE LACE AND RIBBON AND GIRLY STUFF.

IT'S VERY NICE, THOUGH, IF I DO SAY SO MYSELF!

I JUST HOPE IT'S NICE ENOUGH TO WIN THAT PONY.

LISA! ARE YOU STILL UP HERE IN THE ATTIC?

I CAN'T LET MOM SEE THIS! SHE MIGHT KILL ME WHEN SHE SEES WHAT I DID TO HER *DRESS!*

WHAT IF SHE *GROUNDS* ME FOR CUTTING IT UP? I'D NEVER SEE PRINCESS PRECIOUS AGAIN!

CLOMP CLOMP CLOMP

OH! IT LOOKS LIKE YOU'VE BEEN MAKING SOMETHING. CAN I SEE?

NO!

I MEAN, IT'S, UM... IT'S YOUR *BIRTHDAY PRESENT!*

28

HO-OH, *MAN*. THIS COSTUME WILL *SHRED* THE COMPETITION!

IT WOULD LOOK *TOTALLY WICKED* WITH A *CHAINSAW* OR *AXE*. I WONDER WHERE--

BART! WHERE ARE YOU?

BANG!

HAMMOCK NETTING

YOU'D BETTER BE GETTING OUT THAT *LAWN MOWER!*

HEY! WHAT'RE YOU DOING WITH MY *BOWLING BALL BAG?*

I'M BUILDING A ROBOT.

AWESOME, ISN'T IT?

I`M IMPRESSED, BOY. WHAT WILL IT DO?

HOMER, IF ALL GOES WELL, I WILL NEVER HAVE TO MOW THE LAWN AGAIN.

WHY DOES IT HAVE A SKIRT? ISN'T THAT SORT OF...YOU KNOW...

SCOTTISH?

HEE HEE... YEAH, THAT'S RIGHT!

MANLY! LIKE *GROUNDSKEEPER WILLIE!*

IN FACT, IF THIS WORKS OUT, YOU CAN BUILD AN ARMY OF ROBOTS TO MOW LAWNS, AND WE'LL PUT MANLY MEN LIKE GROUNDSKEEPER WILLIE OUT OF BUSINESS AND MARCH ON *TO RULE THE WORLD!*

WOO HOO!

WOW. THAT SOUNDS *WAY* MORE AWESOME THAN WINNING A DUMB LITTLE PONY TO MOW THE LAWN.

YOU *GOT IT,* HOMER.

AND YOU KEEP UP THE GOOD WORK, SON. I'M *PROUD* OF YOU.

OHHH...WHY'D HE HAVE TO GO AND SAY THAT?

HE'LL BE SO DISAPPOINTED WHEN I ONLY WIN A DUMB PONY INSTEAD OF DOMINATE THE WORLD...

AW, SO WHAT? HOMER'S DISAPPOINTED IN ME ALL THE TIME. I WOULDN'T WANT TO UPSET THE NATURAL ORDER OF THINGS.

HAMMOCK NETTING

IT'S TIME TO TAKE THIS BABY OUT FOR A *TEST DRIVE*.

THIS HOCKEY MASK WILL HELP DISGUISE ME. NO ONE CAN FIND OUT I'M NOT A *GIRL*.

AS *IF*.

WHOA!

OH, *MAN*. I AM SUDDENLY NOT SO SURE OF MY CHANCES OF WINNING EVEN THAT DUMB LITTLE PONY.

33

OH, NOW, LISA DEAR...I KNOW HOW MUCH YOU LOVE PONIES.

AND THAT OLD PROM DRESS...? I WAS SAVING IT FOR YOU SO YOU MIGHT MAKE SOMETHING FROM IT.

AS FOR THIS CONTEST, I WOULD NEVER WANT YOU TO GO AGAINST YOUR PRINCIPLES, BUT IT'S NOT FOR ME TO TELL YOU WHAT THOSE MIGHT BE.

IF YOU WANT TO ENTER THIS CONTEST, THAT'S UP TO YOU.

I'M SO PROUD OF YOU FOR TELLING ME THE TRUTH, LISA.

LIKE I SAID BEFORE, YOU ARE SMART AND CREATIVE AND HAVE A PURE HEART.

-Snif!

THANKS, MOM.

I'M SORRY I SAID I WAS MAKING YOU A BIRTHDAY PRESENT.

AND I *WILL*, YOU KNOW.

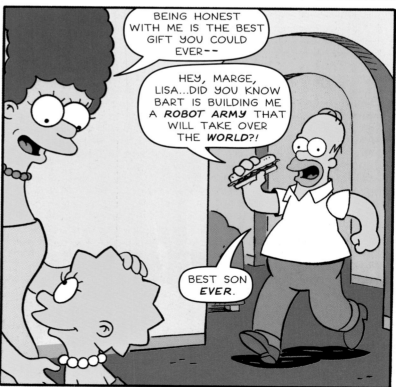

BEING HONEST WITH ME IS THE BEST GIFT YOU COULD EVER--

HEY, MARGE, LISA...DID YOU KNOW BART IS BUILDING ME A *ROBOT ARMY* THAT WILL TAKE OVER THE *WORLD*?!

BEST SON *EVER*.

CHAPTER **3**
JUDGMENT DAY

IN OTHER NEWS, *THE PRINCESS PONYPALOOZA* IS WREAKING HAVOC IN SPRINGFIELD TODAY AS HUNDREDS OF LITTLE GIRLS COMPETE TO WIN *THE PRINCESS PONY FASHION CONTEST*.

TARNISHED TIARAS AND TORN TAFFETA ARE THE *LEAST* OF THE DAMAGE DONE TODAY AS TINY HEARTS BREAK AND SHATTER, ALL FOR THE LOVE OF A PONY.

LET'S TAKE A LOOK WITH OUR LIVE HELICOPTER CAM. *CHOPPER 2*?

THIS IS A HORRIFYING SITUATION, KENT... SCORES OF PRINCESSES ARE ROAMING THE STREETS SLASHING SILK AND RIPPING BODICES.

OH, THE *HUMANITY*!

GOODNESS! I'M GLAD YOU NEVER WENT OUTSIDE WITH YOUR COSTUME, LISA.

ME, *TOO!*

WHAT DO YOU **MEAN**, WE HAVE TO **SHUT DOWN** THE **CONTEST**?

THE PRINCESS PONY COMPANY GAVE YOUR SCHOOL DISTRICT **GOOD MONEY** SO WE COULD **PROMOTE** THIS EVENT!

DEAR GOD, I'M HAVING A FLASHBACK.

LISTEN HERE, COUNTLESS LITTLE GIRLS ARE TRAUMATIZED FOR *LIFE*, RIPPING OFF THEIR OWN GOWNS TO KEEP FROM BEING ATTACKED BY POINTY-TOPPED LITTLE SAVAGES WITH WANDS.

MEDIC!

YOU SIGNED A CONTRACT, CHALMERS, AND WE'RE HOLDING YOU TO IT!

PRINCESS PRECIOUS...

WE DID THIS...FOR YOU...

AND AS LONG AS WE HAVE AT LEAST *TWO VIABLE CONTESTANTS*, WE HAVE A *CONTEST*! *LOOK!* THERE'S ONE *NOW!*

AND YOUR *SECOND CONTESTANT* IS RIGHT HERE.

SHORTLY...

AND NOW THE MOMENT WE'VE ALL BEEN WAITING FOR, THE EVENT FOR WHICH SPRINGFIELD HAS GIVEN HER YOUNGEST AND BRIGHTEST TALENTS...*THE PRINCESS PONYPALOOZA DESIGN CONTEST!*

I WANT POPCORN.

WHY DON'T THEY HAVE POPCORN?

PONIES LIKE POPCORN.

HUSH, HOMER.

AS YOU KNOW, HUNDREDS OF YOUNG LADIES ENTERED THIS CONTEST, BUT DUE TO CIRCUMSTANCES BEYOND OUR CONTROL, ALMOST ALL OF THEM HAVE BEEN ELIMINATED.

SO RATHER THAN MAKING YOU SIT THROUGH EXCRUCIATING TALENT COMPETITIONS AND ENDLESS INTERVIEWS, WE'LL CUT RIGHT TO THE CHASE.

LADIES AND GENTLEMEN, I PRESENT OUR *TOP TWO CONTENDERS* FOR THE *PRINCESS PONY TITLE,* LISA SIMPSON AND BARBARELLA SAMSON!

YAY... CLAP... CLAP...

LISA, I UNDERSTAND YOU CREATED THIS PRINCESS OUTFIT ALL BY YOURSELF!

YES, BUT I'M NOT HERE TO TALK ABOUT THAT.

I WANT TO TALK ABOUT THE *EXPLOITATION* OF YOUNG GIRLS BY THE PRINCESS PONY COMPANY.

40

BART SIMPSON
IN
MOVIE MAYHEM

JAMES BATES WRITER	**MIKE ROTE** INKS	**CHRIS UNGAR** LETTERS
LUIS ESCOBAR PENCILS	**NATHAN HAMILL** COLORS	**BILL MORRISON** EDITS

THAT TAPE'S GOTTA BE UP HERE!

GIVE IT UP, BART. WE'VE LOOKED EVERYWHERE. IT'S JUST A MOVIE.

"ZOMBIE OR NOT ZOMBIE" IS NOT JUST A MOVIE, IT'S A CULT CLASSIC.

YOU CAN'T RENT IT. I TAPED IT OFF OF "COUNT BROCKULA'S MIDNIGHT MONSTER MADNESS STARRING KENT BROCKMAN!"

YOU'LL NEVER FIND IT.

I FOUND IT!

THE SEARCH FOR INVESTORS BEGINS!

...AND *THAT'S* HOW THE ZOMBIES ARE TURNED AWAY BACK INTO THE NIGHT! UNTIL THE SEQUEL, OF COURSE.

UNDEAD MEN WALKING

SO, HOW MUCH CAN WE PUT YOU DOWN FOR..."EXECUTIVE PRODUCER"?

I THINK IT'S GREAT THAT YOU AND MILHOUSE HAVE FOUND SOMETHING FUN TO DO, BUT WE ALREADY GIVE YOU AN *ALLOWANCE* TO BUY STUFF TO *PLAY* WITH.

WE GIVE THE BOY AN ALLOWANCE?

C'MON, DAD!

SORRY. I'M NOT THROWING AWAY THE ONLY MONEY I HAVE LEFT AFTER I PAY YOUR MOTHER ALIMONY ON SOME *SILLY* MOVIE.

I REMEMBER THIS OLD CAMERA! WE FILMED THE STORMING OF NORMANDY WITH IT...OR WAS THAT A STORM AT NORM'S DELI?

THANKS FOR NOTHIN', GRAMPA.

I'M HUNGRY.

ABSOLUTELY NOT! THERE'S NO ROOM IN THE SCHOOL BUDGET FOR KIDS TO USE THEIR IMAGINATIONS.

WE'RE SUNK!

SO NOBODY BELIEVES WE CAN DO THIS. WHO NEEDS THEM?

WE DO. IT COSTS MONEY TO MAKE THINGS BLEED AND BLOW UP.

SHOW TIME!

"IN SPRINGFIELD, U.S.A., IT WAS A CALM AND PEACEFUL SPRING DAY...OR WAS IT?"

"RADIATION LEAKING FROM THE OLD NUCLEAR PLANT FLEW THROUGH THE AIR LIKE AN ANGRY BIRD!"

UNDEAD MEN WALKING

"THE RADIOACTIVITY IN THE AIR WAS ENOUGH TO *WAKE THE...DEAD!!!*"

HOMEY, IT'S JUST A MOVIE.

BUT THIS IS ALL MY FAULT! I KNEW IGNORING ALL THOSE BLINKING RED LIGHTS ON MY CONTROL PANEL FOR ALL THESE YEARS WOULD COME BACK TO BITE ME ON THE BUTT.

OOH, SANTA'S LITTLE HELPER. THIS MUST BE YOUR SCENE.

"THE FIRST TO RISE FROM THEIR GRAVES WERE LOST PETS. UNDEAD AND RABID, THEY *FOAMED* AT THE MOUTH."

THE END

A BART & MILHOUSE JOINT

HMM, I'M SURPRISED THERE WASN'T A STANDING OVATION.

YEAH, WHAT GIVES?

I'LL GIVE YOU CREDIT FOR CLEVERLY STEALING SHOTS OF PEOPLE AND TRYING TO MAKE IT A STORY, BUT...

BUT WHAT?

IT STUNK, BOY.

MOM?

WE LOVE YOU... UNCONDITIONALLY.

MAGGIE, WHAT'D YOU THINK?

SUCK SUCK

DAD? I'M OVER HERE! WAIT!

A NEW LOW FOR YOU, SIMPSON.

WHY COULDN'T YOU SHOOT MY *GOOD* SIDE?

WORST SPECIAL EFFECTS *EVER!*

YOU NEVER GAVE ME THEM PRUNES!

WE WASTED OUR LIFE SAVINGS.

I REALLY THOUGHT IT WAS GOOD.

IT *WAS* GOOD.

WELL, ANGEL, NOW THAT HOMER TOOK THE REST OF THE FAMILY TO MOUNT SPLASHMORE AND ASKED ME TO BABYSIT, WHAT DO YOU WANT TO DO TODAY? ANYTHIN' YOU WANT! THE SKY AND, UH, $17 IS THE LIMIT!

GA-GA-GOO! HEE-HEE!

KRUSTY-BRAND BABY OATMEAL
NOW 38% FEWER RAT DROPPINGS!

≋SNIFF-SNIFF!≋ WHEW! YOU SMELL THAT? THAT'S SOME INTERESTIN' STINK THERE THAT PROBABLY SHOULDN'T COME FROM NO BABY.

SUCK! SUCK!

OH, I GET IT. YEAH, HOMER'S GOTTA LOT OF WEIRD AROMAS SURROUNDIN' HIM.

I THOUGHT I RECOGNIZED THAT SMELL FROM THE BAR.

SUCK! SUCK!

NORMALLY, THE CIGARETTE SMELL, Y'KNOW, SORTA DROWNS IT OUT AND ALL.

C'MON, ANGEL. HERE COMES SONNY TO THE TOLLBOOTH. HEY, C'MON, YOU NORMALLY LOVE THIS CRAP. WHY AIN'TCHA EATIN' IT?

OH, I SEE, YOU WANTED A LITTLE SUGAR THERE ON YOUR OATMEAL. HOMER MUST'VE TOOK THE SUGAR BAG WITH 'EM TO EAT ON THE LOG FLUME. THAT'S ALWAYS BEEN HIS DREAM. OR AT LEAST, AFTER A FEW BEERS, THAT'S WHAT HE *SAYS*. C'MON, WE'LL GO BORROW A CUP OF SUGAR.

SUGAR

AS MR. RITZFIELD'S ATTORNEY, I'D LIKE TO THANK YOU ALL FOR COMING TO THE READING OF THE WILL. OL' GIL IS HOPING FOR SOMETHING TOO. HEH-HEH. I'LL TAKE ANYTHING, EVEN THE FOOD LEFT IN THE FRIDGE! C'MON, THE WOLVES ARE AT OL' GIL'S DOOR!

KNOCK! KNOCK! KNOCK!

EXCUSE ME, SIR. THERE SEEMS TO BE ANOTHER GUEST ARRIVING.

CAN I HELP YOU, SIR?

UH...YEAH. HI YA THERE, JEEVES. WE WAS JUST WONDERIN' IF WE COULD BORROW A CUP OF SUGAR.

I'M SORRY, THE MAN OF THE HOUSE, MR. RITZFIELD, IS RECENTLY DECEASED. YOU'VE COME AT A VERY AWKWARD TIME.

YEAH, WELL IF HE'S DECEASED 'N' ALL, THEN HE WON'T BE NEEDIN' NO SUGAR, WILL HE?

TOUCHÉ, SIR. WELL PLAYED. I SHALL FETCH YOU A CUP. WON'T YOU COME IN?

SUCK! SUCK!

59

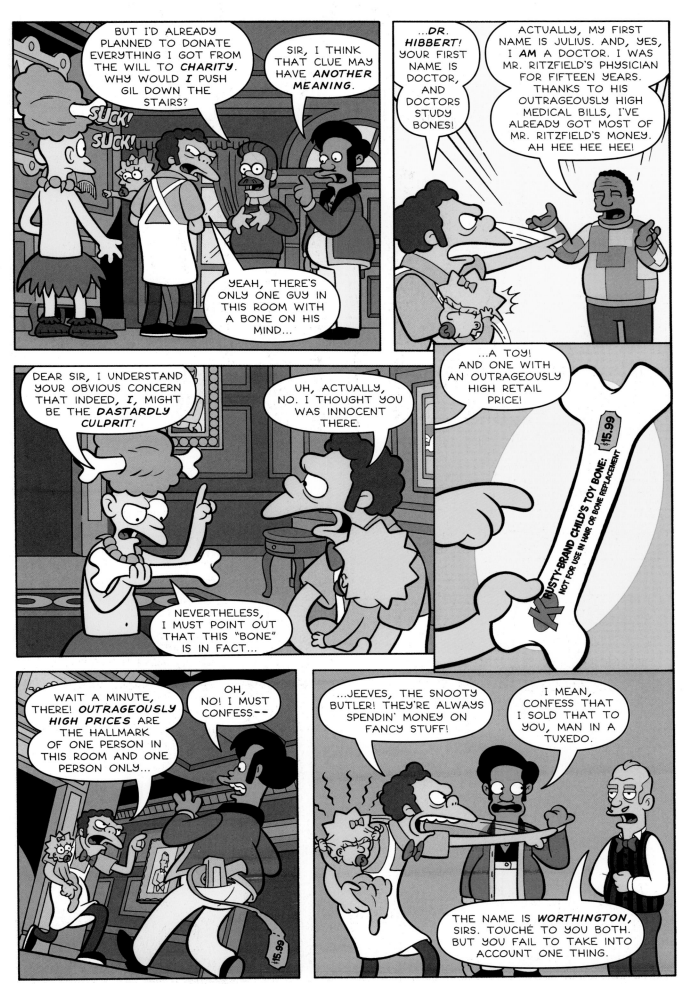

YOU SEE I HAVE A PROSTHETIC LEG. IF I ATTEMPTED TO PUSH ANYONE, THE FORCE OF MY OWN PUSH WOULD KNOCK ME TO THE FLOOR.

THAT DON'T MEAN YA COULDN'T HAVE DONE IT ANYWAY!

:SIGH: THAT'S TRUE, SIR. EXCEPT FOR THE FACT, YOU MIGHT REMEMBER, THAT I WAS STILL IN THE *KITCHEN* WHEN THE LIGHTS WENT OUT. I COULD HARDLY RUN IN AND GET BACK OUT IN THAT SHORT OF TIME.

BOY, THIS IS A REAL MIND TICKLER THERE, ANGEL. NO ONE SEEMS TO GOT NO MOTIVE.

ACTUALLY, I NEVER LIKED GIL. I ONCE THREATENED TO PUSH HIM DOWN THE STAIRS IN PUBLIC. I JUST CANNOT STAND THE MAN!

OH, I'M SORRY. YOU WANNA PLAY WITH YOUR LITTLE FRIEND. AW, THAT'S CUTE.

SUCK! SUCK!

BABY'S FIRST SKELETON

I THINK I GOT THIS MYSTERY ALL WRAPPED UP...

SUCK! SUCK! SUCK! SUCK!

"GIL DIDN'T GET PUSHED DOWN NO STAIRS! HE MUST'VE PANICKED IN THE DARK!"

I, JONATHAN RITZFIELD III, BEING OF SOUND BODY AND MIND, DO HEREBY--

AH! GOSH DARN IT. MUST'VE BLOWN A FUSE.

"THEN, WE HE WENT TO TURN ON THE LIGHTS, HE TRIPPED, AND FELL DOWN THOSE STAIRS! IT WEREN'T NO MURDER! IT WAS AN ACCIDENT!"

DON'T WORRY, OL' GIL WILL--

AAAH!

ACTUALLY, OL' GIL ISN'T EVEN DEAD, AND I WAS LYING RIGHT ON TOP OF THE WILL. HOW DO YA LIKE THAT? THINGS ARE FINALLY LOOKIN' UP!

HE'S A ZOMBIE! KILL HIS BRAIN!

IT'S MY MEDICAL OPINION THAT THIS MAN IS NO ZOMBIE.

OH WELL, MYSTERY SOLVED THEN. WE'D BETTER BE GETTIN' BACK. I GOTTA FEED MAGGIE AND FINISH PEEKIN' INTO THE MEDICINE CABINETS.

OF COURSE, SIR. HERE'S YOUR SUGAR AND THANK YOU FOR "SOLVING" THE MYSTERY.

SUCH THAT IT WAS.

LATER THAT DAY...

WE'RE HOME! WHERE'S MY LITTLE MAGGIE?

AND WHERE'S MY LITTLE MOE?

OW! QUIT IT. OW! QUIT IT!

64

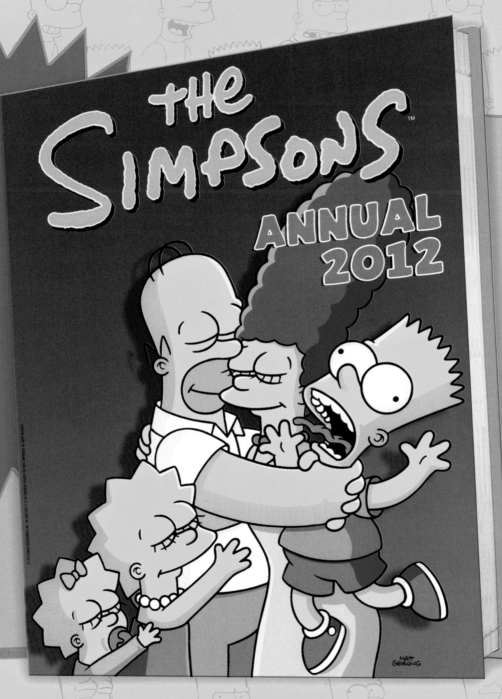